The Day Something Happened

A celebration of our century
by *Blue Peter* viewers

PUFFIN BOOKS

PUFFIN BOOKS

Published by the Penguin Group
Penguin Books Ltd, 27 Wrights Lane, London W8 5TZ, England
Penguin Putnam Inc., 375 Hudson Street, New York, New York 10014, USA
Penguin Books Australia Ltd, Ringwood, Victoria, Australia
Penguin Books Canada Ltd, 10 Alcorn Avenue, Toronto, Ontario, Canada M4V 3B2
Penguin Books (NZ) Ltd, Private Bag 102902, NSMC, Auckland, New Zealand

On the worldwide web at: www.penguin.com

Penguin Books Ltd, Registered Offices: Harmondsworth, Middlesex, England

First published 1999
1 3 5 7 9 10 8 6 4 2

Set in Goudy and Univers

Printed and bound in Great Britain by Butler & Tanner Ltd, Frome and London

British Library Cataloguing in Publication Data
A CIP catalogue record for this book is available from the British Library

ISBN 0–141–30354–9

Contents

Foreword

On 28 September 1998, BBC TV's flagship children's programme, *Blue Peter*, launched a competition, *The Day Something Happened*. Viewers were invited to think about an important or significant event from the last hundred years and to send in their ideas. An amazing 13,882 entries arrived – essays, poems, pictures and cartoons – featuring a huge variety of 'happenings'. Several events had clearly made a deep impression on *Blue Peter* viewers: in particular, the death of Princess Diana, the two World Wars, the sinking of the *Titanic*, the first landing on the moon and World Cup football.

It was enormously difficult to choose just three winners from each age group, but with the help of best-selling children's author Dick King-Smith, along with the *Blue Peter* and Puffin teams, a final decision was eventually made. This book includes the nine prize-winners, as well as some of the very best entries, all by authors and artists aged between four and fifteen.

The Day Something Happened gives a fascinating insight into events that have captured the imaginations of *Blue Peter* viewers. This is their celebration of the twentieth century as we arrive at a new millennium.

Stuart Miles   Konnie Huq

Katy Hill   Simon Thomas

Memorable Events

HMS Titanic *sinks, 14/15 April 1912*

A Bird's-eye View of When the Ship Went Down

I was hungry, I couldn't sleep, a lonely seagull looking
    for food on a cold, dark night.
There was a huge ship on the sea, with the name *Titanic*
    written on its side.
I watched fascinated as it sailed on the sea.
I could hear music coming from the deck and people laughing.
Suddenly, right in front of the ship I saw a huge iceberg!
I called out a warning but they couldn't hear me.
I saw the ship try to steer away, but it was too late.
CRACK!
The ship split in two.
The air filled with screams.
The ship sank.
All was quiet on that cold, dark night.

FIONA CHATBURN AGE 10 SWINDON, WILTSHIRE

SANDY
MCINNES
AGE 11
MUGDOCK,
MILNGAVIE

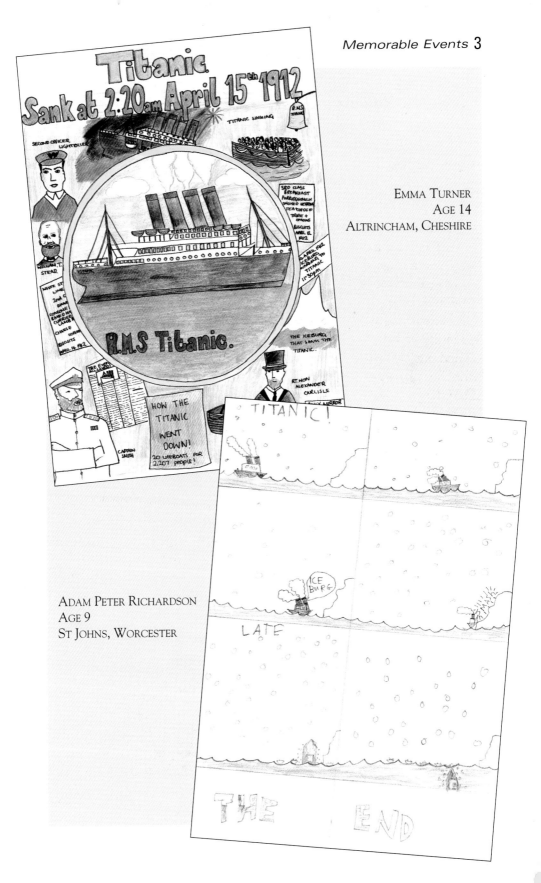

EMMA TURNER
AGE 14
ALTRINCHAM, CHESHIRE

ADAM PETER RICHARDSON
AGE 9
ST JOHNS, WORCESTER

Emily Davison throws herself under the King's horse in protest, 4 June 1913

Derby day 1913

I am Emily Davison.
I am angry that men think that they are more important than women and that women are not allowed to have anything to do with politics or vote in the elections. We suffragettes are raging with anger because we know that men and women are equal.
I am at the Derby waiting for the King's horse to race. Then I will do something that I hope will change the lives of women.
I feel scared. I can hear voices and bustling all around me, a ringing in my ears, the sound of galloping horses......

HOLLY
CAMPBELL
AGE 8
ROYSTON,
HERTFORDSHIRE

Equal voting rights are granted to women in Britain, 2 July 1928

Before World War I Mrs Pankhurst led women in their struggle for the right to vote in parliamentary elections. During this protest women did dramatic things like chaining themselves to walls. One woman was killed running under the king's horse. They starved themselves when they were sent in prison. Then came World War I and they stopped their protests. The men went off to fight and women did their jobs. The suffragettes kept arguing. The government now had to take them seriously. They got tired and gave in. Women had the vote, it had all been worth it.

HELEN PERCIVAL   AGE 7   BRACKLEY, NORTHAMPTONSHIRE

Mickey Mouse appears in the first short animated cartoon, shown on 18 November 1928

Mickey Mouse is the best character in the cartoon world. On this day he Spoke for the first time, in a film called Steamboat willie. he has made every one happy Since then.

FRAZER SHAW   AGE 5   GIFFNOCK, GLASGOW

The first Highway Code is published, 14 April 1931

When my Great Grandad was alive,
He had a car that he could drive.
He shared the road with other wheels,
Bikes, prams, ponies, people delivering bills.
So the Government introduced the Highway Code
To make it safer crossing the road.
If you look in this book,
You will see traffic signs and a list of all the fines.
The code is good at explaining
What to do at a zebra crossing.
Also to be safe at stopping and parking,
And the rules for drinking and driving.
Today there are people still alive
Who may never have survived
If this book had not been done
14 April 1931.

SARAH BUCKNELL   AGE 8   STROUD, GLOUCESTERSHIRE

Premiere of Snow White and the Seven Dwarfs, *the first full-length animated cartoon, 21 December 1937*

LAURA JENKINS AGE 10 SUTTON, SURREY

The Mallard *breaks the speed record for steam engines, 3 July 1938*

It was 3 July 1938 as I sat waiting at our local railway station. The *Mallard* was on her special journey between London and Edinburgh.

The beautiful blue steam locomotive raced past me, she was so big and so loud. (Built in Doncaster, a British design.)

All I could do now was wait and hope that she could do it. So I ran home and waited by the wireless. Then the news came out that the *Mallard* had done it. A new world speed record, 126mph.

And I had seen history made that day by a train.

JAMES RAINE-ELLERKER   AGE 10   BORROWASH, DERBYSHIRE

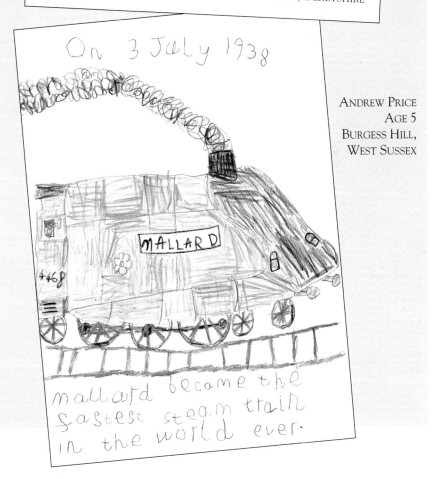

On 3 July 1938

MALLARD
4468

mallard became the fastest steam train in the world ever.

ANDREW PRICE
AGE 5
BURGESS HILL,
WEST SUSSEX

India and Pakistan gain independence, 15 August 1947

DANNY JOHAL AGE 13 WEST BROMWICH, WEST MIDLANDS

Edmund Hillary and Tenzing Norgay reach the summit of Everest, 29 May 1953

The bitter cold crept down my spine and woke me. Tenzing was already up, looking at the Tynaboche Monastery miles below.

At 6.30 we embarked on the treacherous route ahead.

I looked, ice at the east face was in huge cornices which might slip at any second. I felt like a spider climbing a wall about to be blown away, but this was worse. One false move and I'd slip to the Kanshung Glacier. I saw a gap between two rocks. I climbed through. Success! I stood on the summit, Tenzing by my side. We shook hands, then began the descent …

CHRISTOPHER MILLER AGE 10 BIRKBY PARK, WEST YORKSHIRE

The first man on the top of Mount Everest

CHARLOTTE
BARNES
AGE 7
BELFAST

The Coronation of Queen Elizabeth II, 2 June 1953

HANNAH
LOCK
AGE 7
TAUNTON,
SOMERSET

She is the First and Last Queen to be crowned This Century in 19 52.

Queen Elizabeth II

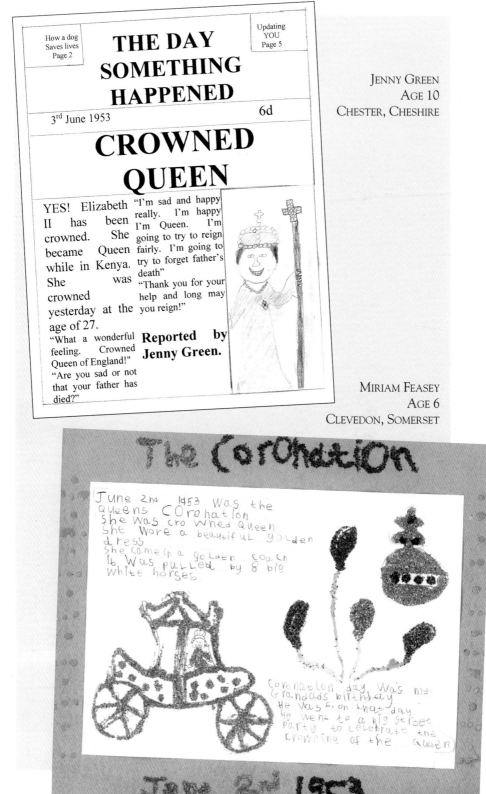

How a dog
Saves lives
Page 2

Updating
YOU
Page 5

THE DAY SOMETHING HAPPENED

3rd June 1953   6d

CROWNED QUEEN

YES! Elizabeth II has been crowned. She became Queen while in Kenya. She was crowned yesterday at the age of 27.

"What a wonderful feeling. Crowned Queen of England!"

"Are you sad or not that your father has died?"

"I'm sad and happy really. I'm happy I'm Queen. I'm going to try to reign fairly. I'm going to try to forget father's death"

"Thank you for your help and long may you reign!"

Reported by Jenny Green.

JENNY GREEN
AGE 10
CHESTER, CHESHIRE

MIRIAM FEASEY
AGE 6
CLEVEDON, SOMERSET

The Coronation

June 2nd 1953 Was the queens Coronation she Was cro Whed Queen she Wore a beaubiful golden dress she come in a golden coach It Was pulled by 8 big white horses

Coronation day Was my Grandads birthday He Was 6 on that day He went to a big street party to celebrate the crowning of the queen

June 2nd 1953

Markie Louise Webb
Age 10
Eynesbury,
Cambridgeshire

Roger Bannister runs a mile in under four minutes, 6 May 1954

The chilly wind that had eased earlier now re-appeared, as if it knew that it had held its breath just long enough. The number 41 began to flutter in an effort to break free from the pin holding it to my vest, but that in turn was vacuumed to my chest, as my lungs squealed and wrenched in order to gain the air that my muscles cried out for. The grey Oxford sky was filled with the cheers of those who had come to witness my achievement – the first human ever to run a mile in under four minutes!

Sam Schofield   Age 10   Bromsgrove, Worcestershire

AILSA DAVIES   AGE 10   LLANSOY, MONMOUTHSHIRE

Notting Hill Carnival Children's Day
(first Carnival held on August Bank Holiday, 1966)

DANIELLE ECCLESHALL-
JOHNSON
AGE 6
COULSDON, SURREY

Patient on the stretcher,
Shaking like a leaf,
I'm having a heart transplant,
I'm getting put to sleep.
Wheeling me off on the stretcher
To the operating room,
Now I'm feeling drowsy,
Opening me up, 1967 is the year.
They took some DNA out,
To stop me getting diseases,
My doctor's name is Christiaan Barnard,
My name is Marty, a teacher aged 25.
I am a success!
I am famous!

STEPHANIE GOW   AGE 9   UXBRIDGE, MIDDLESEX

Britain goes decimal, 15 February 1971

ANGELA DAVENPORT
AGE 14
CONGLETON,
CHESHIRE

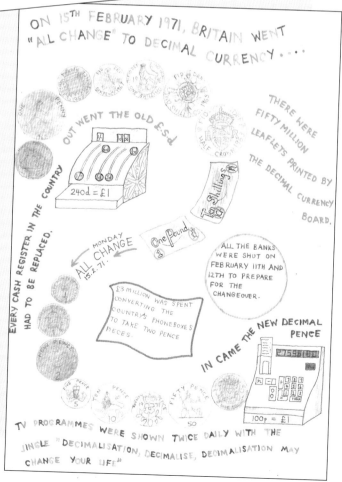

ON 15TH FEBRUARY 1971, BRITAIN WENT "ALL CHANGE" TO DECIMAL CURRENCY....

THERE WERE FIFTY MILLION LEAFLETS PRINTED BY THE DECIMAL CURRENCY BOARD.

OUT WENT THE OLD £.S.d

240d = £1

EVERY CASH REGISTER IN THE COUNTRY HAD TO BE REPLACED.

MONDAY CHANGE 15.2.71.

ALL CHANGE

One Pound

ALL THE BANKS WERE SHUT ON FEBRUARY 11TH AND 12TH TO PREPARE FOR THE CHANGEOVER.

£3 MILLION WAS SPENT CONVERTING THE COUNTRY'S PHONEBOXES TO TAKE TWO PENCE PIECES

IN CAME THE NEW DECIMAL PENCE

100p = £1

TV PROGRAMMES WERE SHOWN TWICE DAILY WITH THE JINGLE "DECIMALISATION, DECIMALISE, DECIMALISATION MAY CHANGE YOUR LIFE"

A hurricane hits Britain, 15/16 October 1987

I thought when mummy Lived in London there was a Big hurricane it Bloow down trees and it Bloow down mummys chimney. The weatherman said there wasnt going to Be a hurricane But there was.

EVE KENNEDY
AGE 6
HOVE,
EAST SUSSEX

WILLIAM BRYAN
AGE 7
BINGLEY, WEST
YORKSHIRE

As I slept
Old ladies wept
As the hurricane blew
But I never knew

The trees were all flattened
By a wind blowing so deep
I said to myself
Thank goodness for sleep!

I woke in the morning
As the day was just dawning
To see such a sight
It gave me a fright

WILLIAM BRYAN AGE 7
BINGLEY, WEST YORKSHIRE

The USA and the USSR sign agreement to reduce nuclear weapons, 8 December 1987

BENJAMIN THOMAS
GRIFFITHS
AGE 10
WOLVERHAMPTON,
WEST MIDLANDS

The Berlin Wall comes down, 9 November 1989

HEATHER GRAHAM AGE 9 STANLEY, CO. DURHAM

The Berlin Wall,
Was not a nice wall
Dividing best friends,
Families and all.
You couldn't escape,
From the east to the west
Staying where you were
was probably best.
The wall was guarded,
Day and night.
If you tried to get over,
You'd get quite a fright.

When the wall was demolished,
In 1989,
The people, they thought
Their luck was just fine.
Many went to collect
Their own souvenirs,
An old, old piece
Of the old Berlin Wall.

KATE FORSHAW AGE 10
SOUTHPORT, MERSEYSIDE

It is New Year's Eve 1989.

I am being drawn towards the wall like thousands of others. They come from all over the world. There is music and dancing, and strangers behave like friends.

Behind the wall in no man's land it is silent. Only the guards patrolling.

Beyond that in East Germany we can hear another party going on. Fireworks fill the air and music can be heard.

Suddenly people climb up on the wall and dance on top.

Hammers and chisels start chipping at the wall. Soon it will be down.

JESSICA DUNN   AGE 9   ELY, CAMBRIDGESHIRE

East and West Germany re-unite and become one country, 3 October 1990

ESTHER BURKE
AGE 15
REDDITCH,
WORCESTERSHIRE

Midnight October 3rd 1990 - Germany is reunited as the Berlin Wall which symbolised Germany's division into two countries East Germany and West Germany is demolished.

Workers on the Channel Tunnel break through the final section, 1 December 1990

HARJIT MEHROKE
AGE 12
HOUNSLOW,
MIDDLESEX

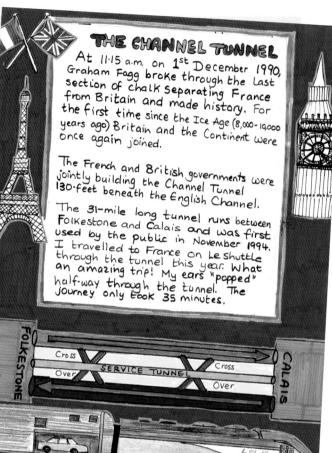

THE CHANNEL TUNNEL

At 11.15 a.m. on 1st December 1990, Graham Fagg broke through the Last section of chalk separating France from Britain and made history. For the first time since the Ice Age (8,000-10,000 years ago) Britain and the Continent were once again joined.

The French and British governments were jointly building the Channel Tunnel 130-feet beneath the English Channel.

The 31-mile long tunnel runs between Folkestone and Calais and was first used by the public in November 1994. I travelled to France on Le Shuttle through the tunnel this year. What an amazing trip! My ears "popped" half-way through the tunnel. The journey only took 35 minutes.

ELISHA BECKMAN
AGE 9
BARROW-IN-
FURNESS,
CUMBRIA

Windsor Castle catches fire, 20 November 1992

ELLIE BINNIE AGE 5 CHELTENHAM, GLOUCESTERSHIRE

*British rule
ends in
Hong Kong,
1 July 1997*

LAURA JIBSON
AGE 7½
HESSLE, EAST
YORKSHIRE

FAREWELL, HONG KONG

Goodbye forever, Hong Kong,
Britain will not rule you
After 99 years .
I can see the tears,
You want your independence back.

I look at your army, your country,
Goodbye to you all, Hong Kong.
I hope I've changed you
Just as much as I can.

I watch your dances, Hong Kong,
The swirling and twirling of dragons,
Bobbing of junks on the sea.
Goodbye, for a long time.

Tonight is the night I own you no more.
I've handed you over, for better, for worse.
Britannia sails on the tide.
The rain comes down with my tears.
SO LONG, HONG KONG!

By Rosie Isbell

ROSIE ISBELL AGE 11 HANHAM, BRISTOL

1st PRIZE Eleven to Fifteen

A special day in 1998

Darkness – I heard voices but there was nothing to see. It was only a bit of fun but I had to complete the course. I had wanted to do it for a long time.

A reassuring voice whispered to me. I can still remember every word, "Just relax, he knows what he's doing." I felt a tug as Karlo stepped forward. Eagerly I followed.

His paws padded softly as he guided me around the obstacles. He was in control.

We stopped. I removed the blindfold. As the crowd applauded I gave Karlo, the newly qualified Guide Dog a hug!

KATIE CURLING AGE 11 CHATHAM, KENT

The signing of the Good Friday Agreement, 10 April 1998

My name is Sean. I live with my mum and three sisters in Belfast in Northern Ireland. My daddy went to heaven three years ago and I miss him very much. Mummy says a lot of people have died since the troubles began many years ago.

Today on the news the man said the IRA will stop doing these terrible things and we will have peace.

It will be nice to see what peace is like.

JAMES WILLIAMS AGE 9 SHREWSBURY, SHROPSHIRE

1st PRIZE Eight to Ten

The Marylebone Cricket Club lets in women members, 28 September 1998

the day something happened

I am writing about the marylbourne cricket club that has not let women join for 211 years.

on the 28th September 1998 the men voted to let women join the club.

I am very pleased because I am a girl and when I grow up I want to be able to do the same things that boys can do.

2nd PRIZE Seven and Under

SATIN POLLARD AGE 5 BRIGHTON, EAST SUSSEX

A Time of War

**The First World War,
4 August 1914–11 November 1918**

Peace on Christmas Day 1914

Long ago during the war
It was 1914 I saw it all
As a tiny mouse, that's what I am
World War I it began.

Horrific scenes
Screams and cries
Thousands killed unidentified.

Trenches built far apart
They were muddy, damp, cold and dark
Shooting continued day and night
Neither side would give up the fight.

Then one morning Christmas Day
Trenches were deserted
Soldiers strayed
Laughter and shaking of hands
Friendly football games on no man's land.

Stunned, amazed
I couldn't believe my eyes
That one Christmas Day
Soldiers stayed alive.

JENNIFER LANGFORD AGE 15 DONCASTER, SOUTH YORKSHIRE

26 August 1914

A young British soldier, Frederick Luke, was fighting in France. The British Army was in retreat, but at Le Cateau they made a stand. Under heavy attack from the German Army and about to lose artillery guns, Fred volunteered to rescue the guns and rode out with six others. Of the seven, only Captain Reynolds, Job Drain and Fred returned, but they saved one of the guns.

For this bravery they were all given the Victoria Cross.

Fred Luke was my great-grandfather and although he died before I was born, I am proud of his bravery on that day.

SAMANTHA LUKE AGE 10 LANGPORT, SOMERSET

The Second World War,
3 September 1939–15 August 1945

MAX CONWAY
AGE 7
SOUTHEND-
ON-SEA, ESSEX

The First Air Raids

On August 7 1940 German planes flew over my grandparents' home My grandmother hid under the table with their baby (my uncle). My granddad went outside to watch the planes! They dropped leaflets! Three weeks later, on August 30th, the house was destroyed in Manchester's first heavy bombing raid, whilst they were in the Anderson bomb shelter in the garden.

Anne Frank is given a diary, 12 June 1942.
It is first published in 1947.

Anne Frank woke at six o'clock in the morning of Friday 12 June. It was wartime, 1942. It was her thirteenth birthday. Anne lived in Amsterdam. The Germans had launched a campaign of discrimination against the Jews, so that made it hard for them, but she did not think about it.

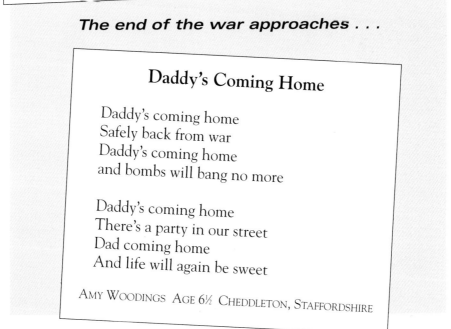

Anne received lots of presents, but there was one best of all. It was a red checked hardback diary. She had never had a diary before. When Anne received this present she never dreamt that one day millions of people would be reading her diary.

DANIELLE TOSTEVIN AGE 12 STOWMARKET, SUFFOLK

The end of the war approaches . . .

Daddy's Coming Home

Daddy's coming home
Safely back from war
Daddy's coming home
and bombs will bang no more

Daddy's coming home
There's a party in our street
Dad coming home
And life will again be sweet

AMY WOODINGS AGE 6½ CHEDDLETON, STAFFORDSHIRE

STUART FLEGG
AGE 6
LYTHAM
ST ANNES,
LANCASHIRE

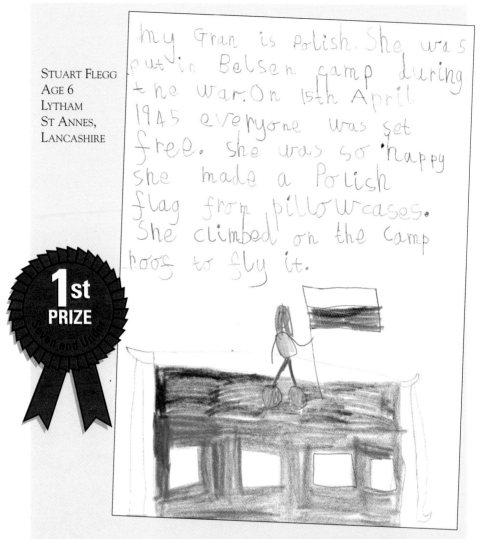

my Gran is Polish. She was put in Belsen camp during the war. On 15th April 1945 everyone was set free. She was so happy she made a Polish flag from pillowcases. She climbed on the camp roof to fly it.

1st PRIZE
Seven and Under

VE (Victory in Europe) Day, 8 May 1945

The Day the War Ended

The faces of the people gathered here in the square
Show the joy, the happiness, the pain and despair.
The long years of war were painful to bear
But just for this moment the crowd doesn't care.

The enemy defeated, Our Boys home at last,
Soon all the bad times will be memories of the past.
The chimes of Big Ben, the bells of St Paul's,
The flags and the streamers, it's victory for all.

Let's not forget the ones who will stay
In the battlefields of Europe for ever and a day.
But just for this moment this crowd doesn't care,
'Victory is ours' – their cries fill the air.

KATHRYN FOWLER   AGE 9   GRIMSBY, LINCOLNSHIRE

HANNAH KEARNS
AGE 10
SOUTHAMPTON,
HAMPSHIRE

Hello, my name is Albert. This is my story of 8 May 1945. That day as usual I went on my paper round. All the headlines proclaimed the end of World War II in Europe.

My first stop was at a posh house owned by Edwina Brown. She usually snapped at me but today she had a friendly smile. However, next door Cyril was very sad. He had been informed his son was missing.

Suddenly I was carried away on a crowd of people towards Buckingham Palace. They waved flags and cheered. I was next to a young girl in uniform who looked familiar. As we came to the palace I saw Cyril crying with happiness hugging his son. When Princess Elizabeth came on to the balcony I felt I knew her from somewhere.

GRACE STEPHENSON   AGE 7   SHREWSBURY, SHROPSHIRE

I'll never forget that day in May 1945. We had the best street party ever. The war was over. There were flags outside people's houses and lots of tables and chairs lined our street. It was a sunny day and we all had a lot of fun even though it was mainly women and children.

We had egg sandwiches, lemonade, Coca-Cola and with some of the left-over rations we made fairy cakes. Me and my friends sat at our own table. We played games and sang songs. What a great party!

CLAIRE BRAKE AGE 9 ROCHESTER, KENT

Remembrance Sunday, also known as 'Poppy Day'

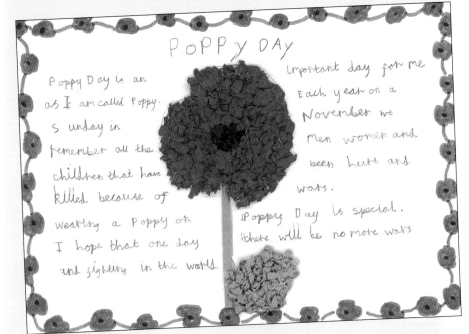

POPPY DAY

Poppy Day is an as I am called Poppy. Sunday in remember all the children that have killed because of wearing a poppy or I hope that one day and fighting in the world.

Important day for me Each year on a November we men women and been hurt and wars. Poppy Day is special. there will be no more wars

POPPY MAXWELL AGE 6 OXFORD

The Falklands War, 2 April–14 June 1982

The Falklands War started on 2 April 1982. My daddy had just come home from a ship and had to go. His mates and him were frightened. The other men were from Argentina. Lots of people died. My dad was in a Sea King that carried food and guns to the soldiers. Hundreds of men were on the England side. Many men were injured. England won the battle. England's men are still on the Falkland Islands. Lots of boys like me lost their daddies but I'm glad my daddy came home again.

SCOTT FRANCIS AGE 6 YEOVIL, SOMERSET

On 2 April 1982 a group of islands that not many people had heard of was invaded by an Argentine force. It was the day the Falklands War started. A message from Port Stanley's telex operator read 'WE HAVE LOTS OF NEW FRIENDS.' After 74 days of fighting and a loss of 264 Allied lives, on 14 June 1982 Argentina surrendered. Now everybody knows where the Falkland Islands are. Such a pity we had to find out this way.

ANDREW MCTOMINEY AGE 7 MIDDLESBROUGH, CLEVELAND

Inventions and Discoveries

The Model T Ford, the first mass-produced car, goes on sale, 12 August 1908

Today something really exciting happened. The first Model T Ford came off the production line and I've bought one, the first one. Gee, it is beautiful. It is all shiny metal and leather seats. You're probably thinking that I'd have to be rich to afford an automobile but you'd be wrong. I'm just a worker at the Detroit Ford plant. The thing is that the Model T is the first car that an average person can afford. Henry Ford says that it will revolutionize the automotive industry but I think it will revolutionize the whole world. Soon everybody will have a car and the world will be a better place for it. Now I'm off for a drive.

NAOMI R. STEVENS   AGE 15   BELFAST

The first practical demonstration of television takes place, shown by John Logie Baird, 26 January 1926

Dear Diary
Today was so exciting and interesting. I was taken to the Royal Institution by my father, to see a new invention by John Baird. 'This is a new machine capable of transmitting moving pictures into the home, called television.'

I was amazed and felt very privileged. The quality of the picture is not as good as the cinemas, but it is early days. Baird hopes that one day there will be a television in every home.

It is spectacular but some people disagree, so we will all have to wait and see what happens.

VICTORIA RIDLEY   AGE 13   EASINGWOLD, YORKSHIRE

The Television

Pictures, stories, news and fun
When our television's on.
Music, dancing, colour, sound
Magic boxes all around.
Across the world it beams its light
The television, day and night.
It changed our lives when it was born,
The breaking of a brand-new dawn.
Animals, people, games and weather,
The television is here for ever.

DAVID MALKIN   AGE 6   MOULTON, LINCOLNSHIRE

Penicillin is discovered by Alexander Fleming, 30 September 1928

CATIE WALKER   AGE 9   LOWESTOFT, SUFFOLK

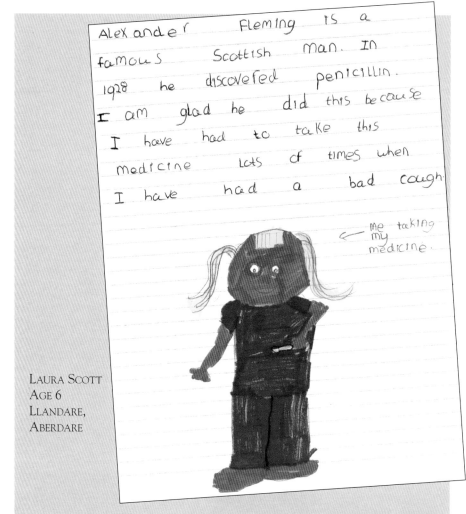

Alexander Fleming is a famous Scottish man. In 1928 he discovered penicillin. I am glad he did this because I have had to take this medicine lots of times when I have had a bad cough.

← me taking my medicine.

LAURA SCOTT
AGE 6
LLANDARE,
ABERDARE

The discovery of DNA, 25 April 1953

James Watson and Francis Crick may not be the most well-known people in the world but if it wasn't for them the world's population would not be as it is today. In 1953 these two scientists discovered DNA, the building blocks of all life forms. Their achievement was recognized so highly that in 1962 they were awarded the Nobel Prize for Physiology and Medicine. In today's world, police work strongly relies on the findings of DNA evidence, as do other professionals like archaeologists and historians. Since then this science has been applied to many other areas of life.

ADAM BUTTERFIELD AGE 14 LONDON

STEVEN TRAN AGE 13 COLWYN BAY, CLWYD

Flight and Space Travel

Wilbur and Orville Wright make the first powered aeroplane flight, 17 December 1903

I see the world before me
Surely this must be a dream
I am an oasis in a desert of sand:
Flying, gliding it seems.

Around me is a myriad of blue,
White clouds floating before my eyes
Soaring on wings, I feel as if I'm king
And land is a far-away surprise.

The sky is there for the taking
The sun inviting to be tamed.
Through the tears that misted my thoughts
I knew history was mine to be made.

YUENING ZHANG AGE 15 NOTTINGHAM

The Worlds First Plane Flight.

My name is orville Wright

I'm ready to go on the worlds first flight.

It's the seventeenth of December 1903,

'Flyer' my aeroplane is waiting for me.

Off I go up into the sky

Just twelve short seconds soaring so high.

Then back down to earth, skidding along the ground,

There's so much to be discovered, what will be found?

Today is The Day That Something Happened

I have changed the world for ever.

CHRIS MANSFIELD AGE 7 SHEPLEY, WEST YORKSHIRE

Amy Johnson is the first woman to fly solo from England to Australia, 5 May 1930

The Day Something happened

on May 5 1930 an English Lady called Amy Johnson flew in her aeroplane from London to Australia. Her aeroplane was called 'Jason'. She was the first Woman to fly solo from England to Australia and it took 19 days. The British press called her "Queen of the Air". the End.

HANNAH BARRELL AGE 6 SUTTON COLDFIELD, WEST MIDLANDS

HANNAH BARRELL AGE 6 SUTTON COLDFIELD, WEST MIDLANDS

The first living creature in space,
3 November 1957

Hi, my name's Laika. I'm a Russian dog. I left Earth on 3 November 1957 in a spaceship, Sputnik 2. Unfortunately the men who sent me into space couldn't bring me down. So I'm still here getting a great view of the stars.

At times I miss playing with children, sticks being thrown and swimming in the Volga. Even now I'm watching men build a space station and I've seen them walking on the Moon. I am really hoping that man will be able to bring me back to Earth one day.

DEANNA TURNBULL AGE 7 MICKLEHURST, GREATER MANCHESTER

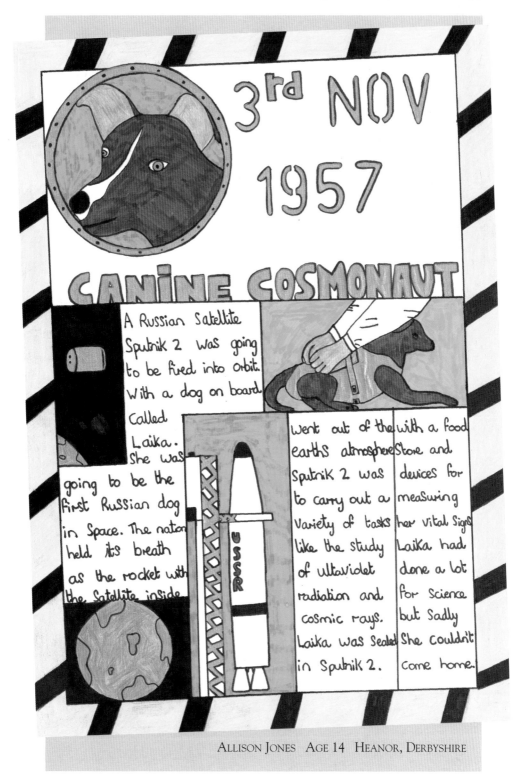

3rd NOV 1957

CANINE COSMONAUT

A Russian Satellite Sputnik 2 was going to be fired into orbit. With a dog on board. Called Laika. She was going to be the first Russian dog in Space. The nation held its breath as the rocket with the satellite inside

went out of the earths atmosphere Sputnik 2 was to carry out a variety of tasks like the study of ultraviolet radiation and cosmic rays. Laika was sealed in Sputnik 2.

with a food store and devices for measuring her vital signs Laika had done a lot for science but sadly she couldn't come home.

ALLISON JONES   AGE 14   HEANOR, DERBYSHIRE

Yuri Gagarin makes the first flight into space, 12 April 1961

3rd PRIZE
Eight to Ten

LAURIE
CORNWELL
AGE 8
AMPTHILL,
BEDFORDSHIRE

Neil Armstrong takes the first step on to the Moon, 20 July 1969

He slowly came out
into a cold, grey, dusty place,
safe in his comfy white suit.
As though under water,
he climbed down his ladder,
and stepped on to the Moon.
Excited and alone.
'One small step for a man.
One giant leap for mankind.'

JAMES KELLY AGE 7 EXMOUTH, DEVON

The Day it Happened
NeiL ARMSTRoNg LANDeD
ON The moon – 1969

JAMIE LAD
AGE 7
KINGSWINFORD,
WEST MIDLANDS

JOEL BALDWIN
AGE 6
BAMFURLONG,
LANCASHIRE

Concorde, the first supersonic passenger aircraft, goes into service, 21 January 1976

THOMAS WHITE
AGE 8
WALSALL,
WEST MIDLANDS

JAMES PARSONS
AGE 6
BOREHAM, ESSEX

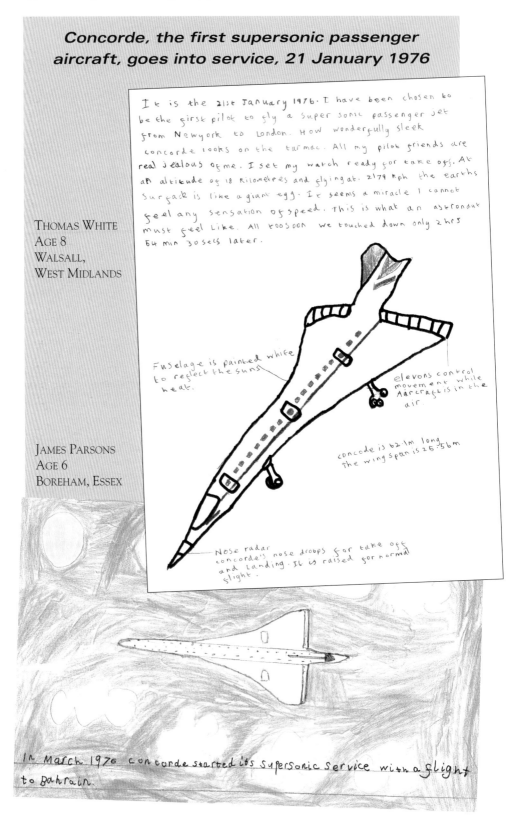

It is the 21st January 1976. I have been chosen to be the first pilot to fly a super sonic passenger jet from New york to London. How wonderfully sleek concorde looks on the tarmac. All my pilot friends are real jealous of me. I set my watch ready for take off. At an altitude of 18 kilometres and flying at 2179 kph the earths surface is like a giant egg. It seems a miracle I cannot feel any sensation of speed. This is what an astronaut must feel like. All too soon we touched down only 2 hrs 54 min 30 secs later.

Fuselage is painted white to reflect the suns heat.

elevons control movement while Aircraft is in the air.

concode is 62.1m long. The wing span is 25.56m

Nose radar concorde's nose droops for take off and landing. It is raised for normal flight.

In March 1976 concorde started its supersonic service with a flight to Bahrain.

Helen Sharman is the first British woman in space, 18 May 1991

1991 is important to me because it was the year that I was born.
Helen Sharman is important to me because of the special thing that she did.

May 18th 1991

Helen Sharman became the first British astronaut. She blasted off from Baikonur, USSR with 2 Soviet cosmonauts in the Soyuz space craft on an 8 day mission to the Mir space station. She returned to Earth May 26th.

ABIGAIL SARAH THOMSON   AGE 7   EDINBURGH

World Cup Football

Long ago in 1966 there were …

Red and white flags waving,
Sun shining,
Crowds cheering,
Teams running,
Goalies saving,
Geoff Hurst scoring,
Goal number three counting,
Referee whistle-blowing,
Pitch invading,
Bobby Moore cup-lifting …

When England won the World Cup.

CATHY SCOTT   AGE 7
LLANDARE, ABERDARE

**The World Cup
Final, 30 July
1966**

DOUGLAS HUNT
AGE 6
SOUTH NORWOOD,
LONDON

The Day England Won the World Cup

In 1966 England were in the World Cup final. Both my grandad and grandpa were there. My grandpa still has the ticket and treasures it greatly. The German supporters were outnumbered and the noise was terrible. It was a sunny day. Germany scored first and the young man in front of Grandpa began to cry, so Grandpa said in the records of the World Cup final the first team to score has always lost. That cheered him up a bit and England did finally win 4–2. The English goals were scored by Sir Geoff Hurst and Martin Peters.

ROSS CLEAVER   AGE 8   EAST GRINSTEAD, WEST SUSSEX

ANTHONY
GAMBLE
AGE 10
CHIPPENHAM,
WILTSHIRE

England play Argentina in a World Cup match, 30 June 1998

England v. Argentina –
Beckham's Point of View

The whistle blew and I lay still,
Face down upon the ground,
I was tripped up in this World Cup
And now I looked around.

Would I be seen if I got mean,
My temper now was growing,
Right foot up in this World Cup,
I knew where he was going.

With rising force, I aimed of course,
The crowd was really humming,
'Beckham, you fool, you broke the rule,'
I knew just what was coming.

Whistle blowing, red card showing,
The anger of the crowd,
I had stuffed up in this World Cup.
I left the pitch head bowed.

JOSHUA CLARK AGE 8
ST NEOTS, CAMBRIDGESHIRE

2nd PRIZE
Eight to Ten

The Day I Remember Most

'And Beckham has got the dreaded red card …'

'He lost it for England!'

I remember the day when England lost the World Cup. I was so upset.

That day I felt like crying. Just the thought of England killed me. That night I couldn't sleep. All I thought about was the Cup going to some other team that I had no intention of supporting. The next day everyone was talking about it. It was weird, high hopes turning into nothing but misery and anger. I think they will do better next time.

CARLIE BRAIDEN   AGE 11   TELFORD, SHROPSHIRE

People We Remember

A. A. Milne (1882–1956), creator of Winnie-the-Pooh, *first published in 1926*

On the 14 October 1926 my daddy bought me a book. It was about my cuddly toys, Winnie the Pooh, Piglet, Tigger, Eeyore, Rabbit, Owl, Kanga, Roo, and ME! My daddy wrote the book after he had told me some imaginary stories about me and my toys. All my favourite stories were there and my daddy's friend, Mr Shepard, had drawn some colourful pictures in the book aswell. Now lots of other children can read the stories about my favourite bear, Winnie the Pooh, and his friends, and I hope they enjoy the stories as much as I do

Christopher Robin Milne

KATIE MACKENZIE   AGE 6   SHIRLEY, SURREY

Mohandas Gandhi (1869–1948), leader of the movement for Indian independence

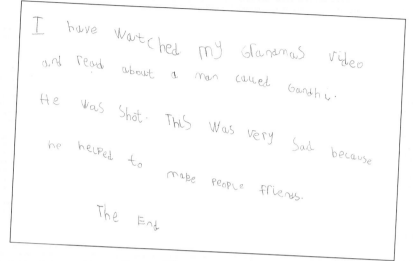

I have watched my Granmas video and read about a man called Gandhi.

He was shot. This was very sad because he helped to make people friens.

The End

BRIONY STEELE AGE 4 RUGBY, WARWICKSHIRE

Martin Luther King (1929–1968), American civil rights campaigner, makes his famous speech, 28 August 1963

I'm writing about the day Martin Luther King made his famous 'I have a dream' speech. The day was 28 August 1963. I'm writing about him because he made a change in the world. On this day 200,000 people marched on the capital of America, Washington. At the end of the march Rev. King made his famous speech. This speech helped to stop people being nasty to each other just because of the colour of their skin. He taught us not to judge people by the colour of their skin but by what was inside them. We should judge them by if they have got a good or evil heart.

AMYCE SMITH-BANNISTER AGE 7 ASCOT, BERKSHIRE

The King Once Said

Martin Luther King once said
'I have a dream.'
His dream was that every one,
Was born equal underneath our sun.

In the world today his speech is all around,
But when we learn it in the class
Do we understand, or do we just agree.
The meaning of his speech was meant for all to see.

On 28 August 1963
King read his speech to 200,000 people.
Each one believing in his words just as much as me.
It was the speech of civil rights
With overwhelming sights.

In today's society the words are said
But the true meaning never read.

AMBER HOMES   AGE 14   BARNET, HERTFORDSHIRE

2nd PRIZE
Eleven to Fifteen

JACOB
FERGUSON-LOBO
AGE 6
BARNET,
HERTFORDSHIRE

Bob Geldof organizes the Live Aid concert, 13 July 1985

I was watching television one day when a rather scruffy-looking man appeared talking about starving people in Africa. His name was Bob Geldof. He was a pop singer. He said he was going to invite lots of other pop stars to make a special record to raise money for Africa. The way he talked made people believe that something could be done. The record was called 'Feed the World' and sold millions of copies. Something special was about to happen. People helped from all over the world, and showed what somebody could do if they cared enough about something.

LARA VICTORIA CROWLEY AGE 8 STEVENAGE, HERTFORDSHIRE

Terry Waite is released from captivity, 18 November 1991

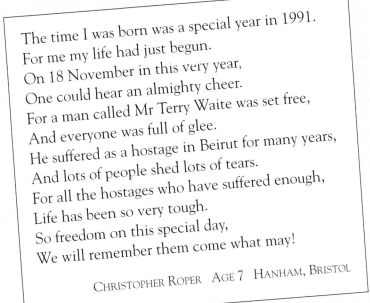

The time I was born was a special year in 1991.
For me my life had just begun.
On 18 November in this very year,
One could hear an almighty cheer.
For a man called Mr Terry Waite was set free,
And everyone was full of glee.
He suffered as a hostage in Beirut for many years,
And lots of people shed lots of tears.
For all the hostages who have suffered enough,
Life has been so very tough.
So freedom on this special day,
We will remember them come what may!

CHRISTOPHER ROPER AGE 7 HANHAM, BRISTOL

Nelson Mandela is released on 11 February 1990. He becomes President of South Africa on 10 May 1994.

My name is Mandela, Nelson,
I spent 25 years in prison.
I was cast aside,
Because of apartheid.

Just because I'm black, not white,
I was locked away from the light.
People can now realize,
There was no truth behind those lies.

I tried to prove I'm the same,
'No different,' I always say.
I'm no different, can't you see?
At last they set me free.

My life was very unfair,
It felt like no one had a care.
I was cast aside,
Because of apartheid.

In the year 1994,
People finally saw.
President of South Africa I became,
Now, people can look back in shame.

My name is Mandela, Nelson,
I spent 25 years in prison.
I was cast aside,
Because of apartheid.

CATRIN ROGERS   AGE 12   RUTHIN, DENBIGHSHIRE

SIÂN PRATTEN   AGE 10   LLANGYNIDR, POWYS

Tony Blair becomes Prime Minister on 2 May 1997

HANNAH WEST   AGE 7   CADOXTON, NEATH

Mo Mowlam becomes Secretary of State for Northern Ireland, 5 May 1997

The day Mo Mowlam became 'Mother' to Northern Ireland

The news said there was a bombing. That's the way it always was, when I watched. Children left without a daddy. People left without a home. I worried, could this happen to me? Mommy said this would not happen to us.

Then one day the news said Mo Mowlam was to be the boss of Northern Ireland. There was talk that fighting would stop. Mommy said she was our best hope because she was strong and fair, like mothers are.

Since she came there has been a change. The news talks of ceasefires. Mo is playing Mother and making peace.

CAOLÁN SHIVERS   AGE 7   TOOMEBRIDGE, CO. ANTRIM

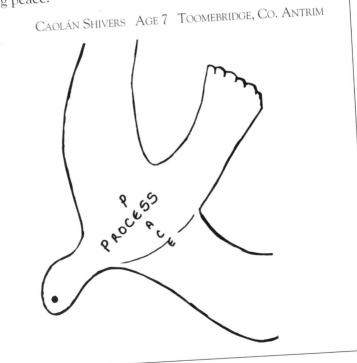

Sad Memories

Many children were affected by the terrible events which took place in Dunblane on 13 March 1996

Just an ordinary day, so everyone thought until Thomas Hamilton entered Dunblane Primary School and shot 16 innocent children and their teacher.

It wasn't until after school that I heard the news. I turned on the television and couldn't believe my eyes. The pictures of grieving parents, flowers, sadness and worst of all the little children's smiling faces filled the screen.

Why had it happened? I thought that you were safe at school. Crossing roads and talking to strangers were dangerous but not going to school.

When Mum came home she hugged me very tightly. We both cried.

ANIKA RANDALL   AGE 12   HALL GREEN, BIRMINGHAM

When I heard about the shooting in Dunblane I thought it was a game or a joke. Surely nobody would shoot children like me. But when I saw pictures in the papers I was very sad. Mum told me he was a bad man and that he will go to a bad place. It makes me sad to think that they are not here to play, like we all should at 6½ years old. Mum tells me that they are playing in heaven. I hope that they are safe up there.

SIONED ELIN CHARTERS AGE 6½ BALA, GWYNEDD

In memory of the children who died at Dunblane March 1996

SAM BASON AGE 7 WEST WICKHAM, KENT

The death of Princess Diana, on 31 August 1997, was another very sad memory for Blue Peter viewers

The Princess

I remember when my mum told me Princess Diana had died. I felt I should cry. Diana was on the news on all the channels. My friend said, 'Did you hear about Diana?' None of us knew her. We thought she was beautiful. Everyone brought her flowers. I felt sad that she died. I feel sorry for her children, William and Harry. I think everyone should remember her and the good things she did.

JORDANNE MEARS   AGE 7   EVINGTON, LEICESTER

DANI EVANS   AGE 6   LEIGH-ON-SEA, ESSEX

CHARLOTTE
LLOYD
AGE 6
BROMYARD,
HEREFORDSHIRE

Diana

Diana our princess has gone to rest
With loads of people having been blessed.
By her thoughts and her love they coped all the more
With problems and illness that no one foresaw.

Name in the newspapers, magazines and books,
Pictures and people admiring her looks.
From country to country she helped all the poor,
She broke down the boundaries of international law.

On the day that she died the world had to share,
That someone so precious was no longer there.
I will never forget the tears that we cried,
On learning that Princess Diana had died.

This day will for me remain in my mind,
As being an occasion of no other kind.
Of one thing I'm sure, for the rest of my days,
I will remember Diana in so many ways.

AMY LAWRENCE   AGE 11   GREAT DUNMOW, ESSEX

31st August 1997

Princess Diana was a very kind and beautiful Princess. She loved children and used to collect lots of money for people who were sick.

Princess Diana died in a car crash on 31st August 1997. Everyone cried because they were really sad and gave her millions of flowers and money to her charity.

I think Princess Diana is happy now in heaven.

INDY
MEHROKE
AGE 7
HOUNSLOW,
MIDDLESEX

Everyone at *Blue Peter* and Puffin
would like to thank the 13,882 children
who sent in their ideas for
The Day Something Happened.